DAN FRONTIER AND
THE NEW
HOUSE

by
William Hurley
illustrations
Don Simmons

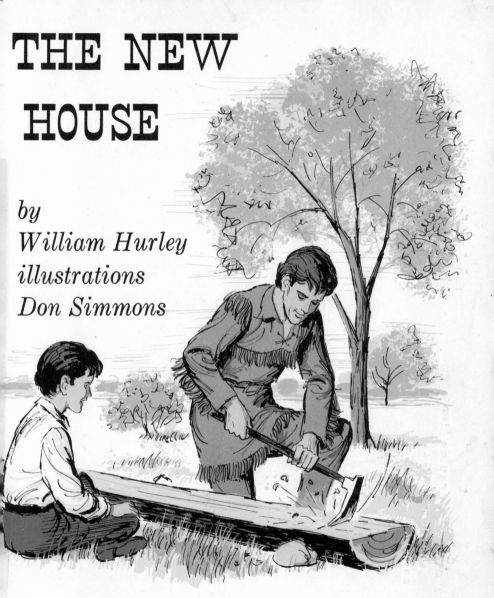

BENEFIC PRESS · CHICAGO
Publishing Division of Beckley-Cardy Company

Atlanta   Dallas   Long Beach   Portland

Library of Congress
Number 61-7678

Copyright 1961 by Benefic Press
All Rights Reserved
Printed in the United States of America

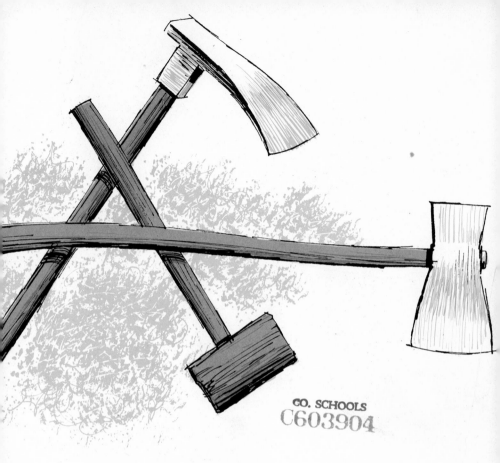

STORIES

Dan Frontier

This is Dan Frontier.

This is Dan's farm.

Dan's farm is big.

King is Dan's horse.

King is a big horse.

"Come, King," said Dan Frontier.

"There is Bill," said Dan to King.
"Come here, Dan," said Bill.

"Look!" said Bill.

"Here comes a wagon."

"Come, Bill," said Dan.

"Get a horse."

Away went Dan.
Away went Bill.

The Nelsons

"I am Dan Frontier," said Dan.

"This is Bill Brown."

"I live in Kettle Creek," said Dan.

"I live in Kettle Creek," Bill said.

"I am Mr. Nelson.

I want to get to Kettle Creek."

"We want to live in Kettle Creek. We want a farm," said Mr. Nelson.

"Come," said Dan Frontier.

"There is a big farm in Kettle Creek."

Kettle Creek Helps

"Here we are!" said Dan Frontier.

"This looks good!" said Mr. Nelson.

"I want this farm."

"I want a house," said Bobby.

Mr. Nelson said, "We will get a house.
We will get a good house."

"We will help you," said Dan.

"We will help you get a house."

"Good," said Mr. Nelson.

"You are here to help, Bill.

I am here, too," Dan said.

"Others must come to help.

Bill, will you get the others to help?"

Away went Bill to Kettle Creek.

Bill went here.   Bill went there.

Bill got help in Kettle Creek.

Bill helped with the house.

Dan helped with the house.

The others helped, too.

Bobby went over to Dan.

"This house looks good," said Bobby.

"This is a good house," said Dan.

The Big Wind

"Dan, look there!" said Bobby.

"Here comes a big wind!"

"Get the horses, Bobby," Dan said.

"Others must help you."

Away went Bobby to get the horses.

"Come, come!" Bobby said.

"Get the horses!

The horses must not run away!"

"Look, look!" called Dan.

"Here comes the big wind.

Go over to the wagons.

Get the horses over there, too."

"Mrs. Nelson, you must not go there.
Run to the wagons," Dan said.
"Look!" said Dan Frontier.
"Look at the big tree!"

"Help, help!" said Bill.

"Come over here.

This horse must have help.

Help get this horse to the wagons."

"Bobby is not here," said Bill.

"Bobby was to come here," said Dan.

"Bobby was to come with the horses.
We must look over there."

Help for Bobby

"Look!" said Bill.
"Here come horses!
Get away, Dan!"

"Look!" said Dan.

"There is Bobby!"

"Bobby!" said Bill.

"Let the horses go."

"Bobby will not let the horses go.
I must help Bobby," said Dan.
Bill said, "Here, I have this.
This will help you."

"Help, help, Dan!" said Bobby.

"I will help you," Dan said.

Bill said, "Here come the horses!"

"I must get the horses," said Dan.

"Dan, you did it!" said Bill.

"You got the horses!"

"I will help Bobby," said Dan.

"Here are the horses."

Dan went to the wagons with Bobby.
"Bobby must have help," Dan said.
Mrs. Nelson said, "We will help.
Here, Bobby, get in the wagon."

C-R-A-S-H, B-O-O-M!!

"There went the house!" said Bill.

"The wind got the house."

"Did the house go?" Mrs. Nelson said.

"We will have to live in the wagon."

"I will help you," said Dan.

"You will not live in a wagon."

"I will help, too," said Bill.

"We will help," said others.

A Good House

"The big wind is over," said Dan.
"Come, we must help the Nelsons.
We must get some trees."

"I want to help, too," said Bobby.

"Bobby," said Mrs. Nelson.

"You must not help.

You must get in the wagon."

Dan and Bill helped with the house.

The others helped, too.

Dan went to see Bobby in the wagon.

"Look at the house," Dan said.

"You will have a house to live in."

Mrs. Nelson said, "Go, Dan.

Go to the others.

Get the others to come here.

We will have fun in this house."

Away went Dan Frontier.

Dan got the others to come.

"Come, have fun!" said Bobby.

"Have fun in the good house."

"This is a good house," said Bobby.

"Dan helped.

The others helped, too."

"We like it here," said Mr. Nelson.

"We like Kettle Creek.

We like this good house."

VOCABULARY

The total vocabulary of this book is forty-four words. Of these, twenty-nine are preprimer level, eleven are primer level, and four are above primer level. Preprimer words are listed in roman type, and those above preprimer are in italics. The words are listed in alphabetical order, and the numbers indicate the pages on which the words first appear.

a 7
am 13
are 18
away 12

big 6

come 8

did 35

farm 6
fun 42

get 11
go 27
good 18
got 22

have 29
helps 18

here 9
horse 7
house 19

I 13
in 14
is 5

let 32
live 14
look 10

must 21

not 26

others 21
over 24

run 26

said 8

the 13
there 9
this 5
to 9
too 21
tree 28

wagon 10
want 15
we 16
went 12
will 19
wind 25
with 23

you 20

DEVELOPMENT OF READING SKILLS

Reading is an important skill integral in learning any subject area. The prerequisite for effective use of reading material is interest. If the child has genuine interest in content, the exercise of reading skills becomes meaningful and enables him to transfer these skills to basic books in any subject.

The supplementary reader provides, in a high-interest story, the exercise and development of reading skills learned in the basic reader.

THE READING SKILLS

I Promoting Growth in Interpretative Skills

Interpreting the main idea

In this story, the Nelson family arrives in Kettle Creek in a covered wagon. Dan Frontier and his friend, Bill Brown, ride out to meet the Nelsons. Mr. Nelson explains that his family wants to settle in Kettle Creek. Dan and Bill offer to help the Nelsons build a house. Many other Kettle Creek men help with the house, too. A damaging storm, injuries, and run-away horses cripple the efforts of everyone for a while, but after much excitement, the new house is completed. Story and beautiful pictures are combined throughout the book to give the child a full under-standing of the main theme. Pages 10, 15-20, 22-23, 28-29, 32, 36-37, 39, 41, 44-45 emphasize the main theme of this frontier story.

Comprehending phrase and sentence meanings

Meaningful narrative helps children to comprehend a scene or action episode and to understand character relationships. From the clear narrative on p. 22, the children will understand the sense of brotherhood that existed among the early frontiersmen. *20-21, 23-24, 27, 38-39, 41, 44-45.

Observing details and understanding their relationship

Details in pictures have special significance at the first-reader level because of the tight vocabulary control and high-interest level of the stories. In the picture on p. 30, the reader will notice that Bill has a rope tied at his waist. On p. 33, Bill gives this rope to Dan Frontier to catch the frightened horses. *36 and 40.

Interpreting a story in sequence

A chain of logically planned events in a story shows the reader how certain hap-penings result in a related action. On p. 13, Dan and Bill meet the Nelsons who have come to Kettle Creek to build a house and start a farm. On p. 23, Dan and the men of Kettle Creek are helping the Nelsons build a house. On p. 25, a storm approaches, and on p. 37 the wind topples the house. Dan and the men of Kettle Creek rebuild the house, and the story ends with a house-warming party on pp. 44-45. *26, 32, 34-36.

Making inferences

Children like to make inferences about what will take place in a story. On p. 33, the reader will infer that Dan is going to lasso the frightened horses.

Forming associations

Children must learn to form the proper associations in order to understand the story theme. Throughout the book the readers will associate the qualities of lead-ership, courage and helpfulness with Dan Frontier. Pages 21, 25, 27-29, 34-35 bear out this association with Dan. *36, 38-39, 42.

Forming sensory images

Situations in a story become almost real to a child if he can form good sensory images. On p. 33, the child will, no doubt, be able to fully imagine the fear and terror that Bobby feels as he is being dragged by the run-away horses. He will also be able to experience the fear and anxiety that Dan and Bill have for Bobby's safety. *28-29, 36, 38, 44-45.

Anticipating outcomes

If a child is reading intelligently, he will be able to anticipate outcomes. On p. 33, Bill hands a lasso to Dan. The child should be able to anticipate what Dan will do.

Making judgments and drawing conclusions

Ability to make proper judgments and conclusions is proof that the child is get-ting the most out of the information he reads. On p. 37, the partially completed house is knocked down by the wind. On the basis of Dan's previous performance, the children should be able to conclude that Dan and the men of Kettle Creek will rebuild the Nelsons' house.

Strengthening memory by observation, association, and visual imagery

Narrative describing the type of work and beautiful pictures showing the country-side, dwellings, and dress of the people in this book help the child to associate this story with the early frontier period. *4-5, 6-7, 10, 15, 24, 27, 41.

II Promoting Growth in Word-Perception Skills

Establishing habits of viewing words in left to right serial order

Children can be helped in mastering the basic left to right reading movement if they practice observing words that begin with the same initial blend, but end differently. Have the children compare words such as "will" on p. 19, "wind" on p. 25, and "with" on p. 23. Also, note "go" on p. 27 and "good" on p. 18.

Observing individual words or phrases in context

Recognition of words and phrases and the understanding of their meaning in relation to contextual material is of primary importance in achieving greater reading skill. On p. 23, Dan is doing something, Bill is doing something, and other men are doing something. They are all "helping."

Strengthening memory of word forms based on association of meaning with printed words, careful observation of visual details, and visual imagery of words

From the printed material and corresponding illustrations on pp. 25-29, the reader can easily associate the word "wind" with the concept of a storm.

Using meaningful clues as an aid in identifying words

Narrative and picture clues on pp. 7 and 8 are a help to the reader in identifying the word "horse." Meaningful clues on p. 8 help the reader identify "wagon."

Developing phonetic skills, auditory perception of rhyme, visual auditory perception of rhyme, auditory perception of initial consonant sounds, substitution of initial consonants and auditory imagery

The children must hear and produce a sound before they can associate it with contextual material. Phonetic helps will speed this process. Point out the rhyming endings but different beginnings of the words "get" on p. 11 and "let" on p. 32.

Developing structural analysis skills . . . recognition of words formed by adding "s" to known root words and recognition of compound words made up of two known root words

Have the children practice known root words first and then the varied forms of those words. For example, have the children first note the word "look" on p. 10 and the word "looks" on p. 18. Note the words "help" and "helped" on pp. 22-23.

Identifying words in capitalized and uncapitalized initial-letter forms

Words in their lower-case forms often cause reading difficulty when they are capitalized. Give the children practice in identifying initial letters.

Testing mastery of sight vocabulary

Practice with words out of context increases the child's sight vocabulary.

III Promoting Growth in Language

Understanding that a sentence is a meaning unit

The use of a word or group of words can express the over-all meaning of a sentence. Note how much meaning and expression the words "Help, help," give to the first sentence on p. 34. *37.

Enriching oral vocabulary

Learning new words and their various meanings helps to enrich the oral vocabulary. Note the different uses of the words "look," and "got" in this book.

* Additional material which will help in developing this reading skill through story material may be found on the following pages: